Chicken!

by Mark Wheeller

A theatre-in-education play for 8-12 year olds

Chicken!
by Mark Wheeller

Author's acknowledgments:

Thanks to StopWatch Theatre Company for their outstanding production of this play, since 1992, and for the "Neighbours" joke.

Cassie Eccles; Chris Gilfoy; Lizzie Hole; Kirsty Housley; Matthew Simpson; Samantha Phillips; Paul Sturrock; Carley Wilson; all students at Oaklands Community School who assisted in developing the original opening section, improvised from my storyline. This scene was re-written by Chris Gilfoy, Matthew Simpson, Samantha Phillips and Mark Wheeller for the 2003 version of the play, which remains pretty much the same in this new edition.

Headteacher and staff at Sinclair and Oakwood Middle Schools, Southampton (1998); Rachael Wheeller for numerous proof readings and general tolerance; John Askew, Local Authority Road Safety Officers' Association; Carol Bagshaw, Hampshire County Council; Martin Ryves, Headteacher, Worton Junior School; Adrian New and Steven Pearce, StopWatch Theatre Company; Dr. Peter Hollis, formerly Headteacher, Oaklands Community School; Meg Davis and Sophie Gorell Barnes of MBA Literary Agents for their continued interest in my work.

First published by **dbda** in 1992 under the title "Why did the Chicken cross the road?".
Updated and reprinted 2003.
This new edition with the title "Chicken!" was first published in 2006.

ISBN 1 902843 19 3

BRITISH LIBRARY CATALOGUING IN PUBLICATION DATA
A catalogue record for this book is available from the British Library.

All enquiries regarding all rights associated with this play, including performing rights, should be addressed to:
Sophie Gorell Barnes, MBA Literary Agents Limited, 62 Grafton Way, London W1P 5LD.
Tel: 020 7387 2076   Fax: 020 7387 2042   E-mail: sophie@mbalit.co.uk

Further copies of this publication can be purchased from:
dbda, Pin Point, 1-2 Rosslyn Crescent, Harrow HA1 2SB.
Tel: 0870 333 7771 Fax: 0870 333 7772 E-mail: info@dbda.co.uk

If, in 1986, I had set out to write my "hit" play it would not have been a Road Safety play. No-one is more surprised than me at the enormous success achieved by **Too Much Punch for Judy** which I wrote, initially, as a 20 minute end section to a Youth Theatre play, ostensibly about alcohol abuse.

The play has been touring in the UK non-stop since 1987[1]. In 1991, I was awarded the *Prince Michael of Kent Special Award for Services to Road Safety Education*. It was this award which inspired the idea of a play for an upper Junior/lower Secondary age group.

I contacted a number of Road Safety Officers in various parts of the country to ask their advice as to what sort of issues such a play should cover. An officer in Hertfordshire suggested that I hold a meeting with teachers from the schools where we planned to perform the play, to find out what their concerns were.

I followed his advice and in the meeting I discovered great enthusiasm on the part of these teachers for the idea of a new Road Safety play. Issues were put forward, many that I had not previously considered. One in particular was common to both schools that would trial the play – the game of "Chicken", where children dare each other to cross the road in front of oncoming traffic. There had already been a death as a result of this problem at one of the schools.

I have to confess that I had gone into this meeting expecting the major issue to be the use of cycle helmets, although I was aware that Hampshire had done a lot of work promoting cycle safety. It transpired that cycle safety issues were far broader than just cycle helmets (although still only a small number of children actually wore them), and the teachers wanted me to try and incorporate a range of basic "safety tips" for cyclists.

I returned home to come up with an outline story for the play, which my Monday afternoon extra curricular Drama group would improvise the following week. I can't say that I spent hours slaving over a hot word processor, but thought about it a lot. Gradually, the story took shape.

---

[1] Full details in the introduction for **Too Much Punch For Judy.**

Introduction

I decided to use the idea I originally had… that of the cycle helmet story, as a red herring, leading the audience to believe that one of the two central characters would end up being killed as a result of refusing to wear the helmet. Then at the end there would be a sudden twist, leading to the other character being hit by a car after being called a "chicken".

I showed the Monday group an outline of this idea and asked them to devise a lively scene showing the lead up to a Christmas day on which two cousins were both given a bike and a helmet. By the end of the scene, their differing attitudes to cycle helmets should be apparent.

The group came back with two improvisations. The best bits from each formed the opening scene for this new play. I was delighted! Although characters and ideas were developed in subsequent meetings, with time running out, I took on the task of writing the remaining scenes in the tradition of slaving over a hot word processor.

By the time a rather hurried draft of my script had been printed we had precisely two weeks until our first performance. We booked a room and rehearsed almost every evening during that period. Everyone worked unbelievably hard and lots of imaginative ideas helped to present this play in the round (which was new to all the cast and greeted with much suspicion!) and (as was intended with this multi-location/zero budget play) without the use of any props… except two cycle helmets!

I felt that the play needed some kind of follow up. However, we did not have time to devise and rehearse a workshop. Hampshire County Council Road Safety Unit and the County Road Safety Officers Association came to our rescue by funding our school's (then) resident *StopWatch Theatre Company,* to devise and run participatory workshops for all the 8-12 year olds who were to see the play.

The title was the final thing to happen. Our working title was **Dean and Danny,** the original names of the two central characters. This was hated by almost all who heard it. When I came up with **Why Did The Chicken Cross The Road?** (the title of this play in its previous editions) I almost dismissed it… but slowly it grew on me and, when other people thought it was "right", the Monday group gave their seal of approval and so the title was finally adopted.

The performances went down very well indeed. The children were gripped and many of the adults who came to see it (we encouraged parents to attend) were in tears! A large number of Road Safety Officers from all over the country came to see the production, all left wanting it to be presented professionally in their areas, except those in our own county of Hampshire who, ironically, remain to this day one of the very few English Counties never to have used the play! I'd love to know why!

StopWatch Theatre Company expressed a serious interest in touring the play professionally. Their ideas, coupled with various hints I had gleaned from Road Safety Officers following the initial performances, led to the second. and much more developed, version of this play being written.

Why Did The Chicken Cross The Road? has almost outdone its predecessor **Too Much Punch For Judy.** It has been performed magnificently by *StopWatch Theatre Company*. In total, it has been performed 4,409 times (most of them by StopWatch) between 1992 and 2006, an average of nearly one every day since it was written (a better average than **Punch**!!!) Their outstanding productions have helped the play to gain a reputation as one that is both educational in content and stylistically interesting to Drama teachers and their school-students.

Three further radical re-writes have occurred since 1992. In 1997, *StopWatch* felt that the 8-13 year olds of 1997 were more "grown up" than the 8-13 year olds of 1992. Also we needed to encourage girls to empathise more closely with the central characters. So Matt had a sex change and became Tammy! This of course, affected all the relationships in the play... Matt's boyfriend became Tammy's girlfriend... Matt's mum became Tammy's dad etc...

In 2006, I was inspired to update the play, when I had the idea of the "Chicken" dare being filmed on a phone camera. In making this change, I decided to do a more general upgrade resulting in this edition of the play. The only similarity this new **Chicken!** (as everyone now calls it, so I've adopted that as the new title) has with the original 1992 play, is the basic sequence of events. Even the end is different from the earliest version of the touring play where the cousin was not killed but received a spinal injury. I guess one lesson to be taken from this is that no play (no matter how successful it may be) is ever "finished". Mine are always "work in

Introduction

progress".

Chicken! was written to be performed by any secondary school age group (ideally for a target audience of 8-12 year olds – although my own 6 and 4 year olds have watched it… and loved it). Equally it makes an unusual choice of play to perform at local or National (NSDF National Student Drama Festival) Festivals! I have found that unusual plays can work to your advantage in competitions/ Festivals such as these!

It is ideal material for GCSE/A' level students to become involved in Theatre in Education presentations working cross phase or within your own school. Alternatively, separate scenes can be used to teach aspects of stagecraft relevant to your exam course. The accident scene is one that may be of particular interest to explore… what different, yet effective ways can your students find to stage this scene?

At my school in Southampton we use the opening scene as one of our "page to stage" exercise for Year 9 students to present. They enjoy the lively nature of the scene and the use of choral speech and choral movement makes an excellent teaching tool for this age group.

Good luck to all who attempt to perform this play. I hope that you will find it challenging and exciting to work on.

Mark Wheeller

Note: The play should be performed with minimum props and maximum imagination.

The Cast (in order of appearance)

Chris Simpson
Tammy Eccles
Ann – Chris' mum
Ray – Tammy's dad
Shopkeeper
Nut-Job (Ian Sturrock)
Massive – Nut-Job's sidekick
Gary Nelson – Tammy's boyfriend
Liz Nelson – Gary's sister

The play has 9 main characters: 4 male, 3 females and 2 of either sex. It can also be presented by two males and two females, in which case the cast should be as follows:

Male 1: Chris and Nut-Job

Male 2: Ray and Gary

Female 1: Tammy and shopkeeper

Female 2: Ann, Liz and Massive

Performances

The first version of this play was first performed by Oaklands Community School "Monday Group" on June 22and 1992. The cast was as follows:

Chris:	Chris Gilfoy	Ian Sturrock:	Chris Claridge
Matt:	Matthew Simpson	Mate:	Daniel Sturrock
Ann:	Kirsty Housley	Linda Ratcliffe:	Cassie Eccles
Sue:	Samantha Phillips	Car Driver:	Carly Wilson
Shopkeeper:	Angie Johnston	Cyclist:	Sarah Ridout

Other parts in the original version played by: Jensen Bourke; Lizzie Hole; Christian Onslow; Kelly Ridout; Paul Severn and Paul Sturrock.

The play received its first professional performance by the Southampton based StopWatch Theatre Company in September 1992.

Section 1:   A Bike for Christmas

As the audience arrive music is playing. Throughout the following scene the two families mirror each other on opposite sides of the stage, each side representing their different homes.

Chris:	*(With a high five.)* Chris!
Tammy:	*(With a high five.)* Tammy!
Tammy & Chris:	Cousins and best mates Chillin' together on the local estates.
Tammy:	Water fights at weekends…
Chris:	… playing knock door run
Tammy:	*(Holding up a phone camera)* Videoing what happens and always having fun!
Chris:	Showing it to our mates next day makes everybody laugh
Tammy:	But if your mum caught sight of them she'd drown you in the bath!
Chris:	She's not that bad!
Tammy:	She's… *well* sad!
Tammy & Chris:	Anyway…
Tammy:	Christmas is coming and there's one thing we'd both like…
Chris:	A state of the art…
Tammy:	… well sorted…
Tammy & Chris:	… mountain bike.
Tammy:	We've dropped some blatant hints
Chris:	… almost every day.
Tammy & Chris:	But if mum/dad's bought one, it's hidden well away. *(NB Throughout choral sections, Tammy says "Dad" and Chris says "Mum")*

Chris:	So a potted introduction has passed before your eye
Tammy & Chris:	And here we are for you today… the "dramatis personae".
Tammy:	There is one little problem though… we're meant to be thirteen
Chris:	Easy… *(To audience)* …suspend your disbelief in every single scene. In Theatre you can conjure up anything at all.
Tammy:	Like what?
Chris:	A microphone
Tammy:	DJ!
Chris:	… Pump it Up!
Tammy:	… Good call!
	(They go into a DJ/rap routine. Tammy soon stops but Chris continues.)
	Chris! *(He finally stops)*
Chris:	At least I don't wear Barbie pyjamas.
Tammy:	Good! Anyway we're here to do this play. So, let's introduce our folks…
Tammy & Chris:	… and get it underway.
Chris:	My mum Ann.
Ann:	Hello! *(As if lighting up her face.)*
Tammy:	And my dad… Ray.
Ray:	Hi! *(As if lighting up his face.)*
Tammy & Chris:	Come on mum/dad tell us, what's the date today?
Ray & Ann:	15th December.

Section 1

All:	Ten more days till Christmas!!!
Tammy & Chris:	Mum/Dad… I'd really like a bike for Christmas.
Ray & Ann:	We'll see…
Tammy & Chris:	You always say *(imitating)* "we'll see".
Ray & Ann:	Well! We'll see! Now time for bed!
Tammy & Chris:	Do I have to?
Ray & Ann:	Yes… or do you want a goodnight kiss?
Tammy & Chris:	Maybe I will go to bed! *(Exit.)*
Ray & Ann:	Catalogue. *(They each grab at a catalogue in their separate homes/sides of the stage. They use an exaggerated style of mime to open it.)* Bicycle pages. *(They point.)* That one! That one! That one! *(Finally they point at the same one.)* That one!!!
Ray:	She'll be ever so pleased with it!
Ann:	I can't wait for his little face to light up when he sees it. *(They come together to denote arrival at the bike shop.)*
Ray & Ann:	*(Indicating sign.)* Bike shop. *(They enter.)* Ting-a ling.
Shopkeeper:	*(Caricature old style shopkeeper, out to fleece the parents for every penny s/he can!).* Greedy shopkeeper. Ah look, some more customers!
Ray:	*(Pointing.)* There it is!
Ann:	That's the one!

Shopkeeper, Ray & Ann:	Suspension front and rear.
Shopkeeper:	Complete with grip shift gears.
Ray & Ann:	Wow!
Shopkeeper:	And…
Ray & Ann:	And?
Shopkeeper:	A lightweight aviation aluminium frame… not to forget the computer contoured saddle.
Ann:	Shaped beautifully for his delicate little bottie!
Ray & Ann:	Can we afford it?
Shopkeeper:	Well, there's the price ticket.
Ray & Ann:	Oh no! Aaaargh! *(Ray faints into Ann's arms and revives pretty much instantaneously)*
Shopkeeper:	Maybe I could offer you a discount?
Ray & Ann:	*(Pulling themselves together.)* We did want that bike for our kids.
Ann:	Christopher…
Ray:	And Tammy.
Ray & Ann:	For Christmas. But we hadn't realised how expensive it was!
Shopkeeper:	Expensive? Ahh. This, my good people, is precision engineering. Quality through and through. You wouldn't want your kids riding through the busy streets of today on any old wheels now… well, would you?
Ray & Ann:	Well, no!
Shopkeeper:	It's guaranteed for 24 months and, as it's

Section 1

	Christmas, I'll give you a five, no, ten per cent discount... if you both buy one! Irresistible don't you say?
Ray & Ann:	A bargain!
Shopkeeper:	But there are a few extras.
Ray & Ann:	Oh no!
Shopkeeper:	Each bike will need lights... front and rear.
Ray & Ann:	Road safety slogan... "Be Safe... Be Seen"!
Shopkeeper:	Fluorescent clothing for the daytime with reflective strips for the night.
Ray & Ann:	Essential... we'll have the lot. *(To audience.)* Can't accuse us of not being safety conscious. *(To Shopkeeper.)* Credit cards?
Shopkeeper:	*(As their hands are full of "stuff" they proffer their back pockets. Shopkeeper takes out the – mimed – credit cards.)* Pop in your pin. *(As s/he slashes their cards.)*
Ray & Ann:	Beep beep beep beep *(as they tap their pin numbers)*
Shopkeeper:	Ting!!! *(Of the till!)* Receipts. Credit cards *(S/he pops the – mimed – receipts into their mouths. Each bites on their receipt.)*
Ray & Ann:	*(Through gritted teeth.)* Thanks.
Shopkeeper:	*(Handing them over.)* Bikes.
Ray & Ann:	*(Through gritted teeth.)* Thanks.
Shopkeeper:	Thank-you. Merry Christmas.
Ray & Ann:	*(Through gritted teeth.)* Merry Christmas to you. *(They make to leave.)*
Shopkeeper:	STOP! Haven't you forgotten something?

Ray & Ann: *(Through gritted teeth.)* What's that?

Shopkeeper: Have a guess?

Ray & Ann: *(Looking suitably puzzled.)* Hmmmmm!

Shopkeeper: Can't you work it out?

Ray & Ann: *(Through gritted teeth.)* No.

Shopkeeper: *(S/he checks with audience until revealing…)*
It's a bicycle helmet.

Ray & Ann: *(Mime spitting out their credit cards enabling them to talk normally again.)*
Oh how could we forget?

Ray: Now we'll have no worries at all! Our kids will be completely safe!

Shopkeeper: Just remember. These features only serve to make the cyclist sa<u>fer</u>. You will still need to remind your kids that their good road sense is the <u>real</u> key to their safety.

Ray & Ann: Right thanks for the advice Shopkeeper.

(As they turn they arrive home.)

Shopkeeper: *(Rubbing hands with glee.)* All part of the service!

(Exits.)

Ray & Ann: Home… Garage… *(Opening the garage door upwards)* Hide the bike.

Tammy & Chris: *(Off stage.)* Hi mum/dad. I'm home.

Ray & Ann: Oh no!

Tammy & Chris: *(Lively entrance.)* Hi mum/dad. I'm home.
(Ray & Ann freeze. There is silence.)
Mum/Dad, where are you?
(They spot their parents.)
What are you doing in the garage?

Section 1

Ray & Ann:	*(Whistling or singing to "cover" obvious guilt.)* Oh nothing!
Tammy & Chris:	What do you mean nothing?
Ray & Ann:	Nothing to do with you.
	(Momentarily freeze action.)
All:	Five more shopping days till Christmas! Aaaaaargh! Shops are packed!
Ray & Ann:	*(Reading shopping list. As they do this Chris & Tammy reach out and put said item into the trolley.)* Potatoes… turkey… Carrots… Sprouts…
Tammy & Chris:	Yeuchh. Chocolate, chocolate, chocolate, chocolate!
Ray & Ann:	Brandy.
Tammy & Chris:	Shandy?
Ray & Ann:	No! You're only 13!
Tammy & Chris:	Ohhhhh!
All:	Now the tree.
Tammy & Chris:	Tree. *(Tammy & Chris point out different trees, using the audience As they do this Ann and Ray find a different fault.)*
Ray & Ann:	Too small.
Tammy & Chris:	Tree.
Ray & Ann:	Too tall.
Tammy & Chris:	Tree.
Ray & Ann:	Too many branches.
Tammy & Chris:	Tree.
Ray & Ann:	No needles.
Tammy & Chris:	Tree.

Ray & Ann:	Let's go and get a plastic one!
All:	*(They struggle to pick up large boxed Christmas trees, Tammy and Chris complaining about the tackiness of plastic trees, their parents ignoring their complaints.)*
	By the window I think.
All:	Decorations.
Ray & Ann:	Lights, baubles…
Tammy & Chris:	… fairy.
All:	It looks even better than the real ones.
Tammy & Chris:	Tacky, cheap and nasty muck.
Ray & Ann:	If you don't stop being rude, Father Christmas won't come and see you!
Tammy & Chris:	*(Mock horror.)* Oh, no!
All:	No more days till Christmas.
Ray & Ann:	It's Christmas day.
Tammy & Chris:	*(To their own parents.)* Merry Christmas!
Ann:	Merry Christmas Chris.
Ray:	Merry Christmas Tammy.
All:	Presents. Exchange. Thanks a lot!
Ray & Ann:	And that's not all. If you look over there you'll see…
Tammy & Chris:	*(Frantically unwrapping.)* Wow!!! A bike!!! Thanks Mum/Dad.
Ray & Ann:	And here's a little something extra!
Tammy:	A cool bicycle helmet. *(Immediately tries it on and does a catwalk turn.)* Does it suit me?

Section 1

Ray:	You look great, Tammy.
Chris:	*(Disappointed.)* Mum. Do I have to wear it? It's gonna kill my cred!
Ann:	Christopher!
Chris:	Mum! Don't call me Christopher!

Section 2: Christmas Outing

Tammy:	*(Wearing her helmet.)* Christmas afternoon, we both arrange to meet.
Tammy & Chris:	*(Chris enters, also wearing helmet.)* "On yer bike at 3 o' clock at the bottom of the street."
Chris:	"You'll miss the Queen do her speech!" me mum she says to me. So, just to please her, I stayed to watch it, then leave at ten past three. "Now wrap up warm… don't want you to catch a chill… And keep that cycle helmet on!"… "Yes mum, course I will!" But once her back is turned… I pull it off my head… *(he does)…* I've got good balance… I won't fall off… I won't come back dead!!!
Tammy:	What kept you Chris… no, don't tell me… your mum made you watch the Queen.
Chris:	Don't be stupid… I was… er… giving my bike a clean.
Tammy:	*(Noticing the bike)* New bike?
Chris:	*(Noticing Tammy's bike)* New bike?
Tammy:	Blatantly!
Chris:	Cool!
Tammy:	Sweet! So… why were you cleaning it?
Chris:	Well, you know Aunt Ermintrude?
Tammy:	My favourite old Aunt…
Tammy & Chris:	… with the knitting needles and the squeaky voice!
Chris:	Yeh, well, I had to find some use for the home-made jumper she sent me.

Section 2

Tammy:	Another one!
Chris:	Yeh, this year it was yellow… with Winnie the Pooh sewn onto it.
Tammy:	With what?
Chris:	Winnie the Pooh!
Tammy:	Nice! You'll never guess what she sent me?
Chris:	I don't know… something cool.
Tammy:	An mp3!
Chris:	I don't believe it!
Tammy:	Can just imagine your mum… "Ooh, isn't that smart. I know… you can wear that when you go to see Uncle Ray and Tammy on Boxing Day. Ooh! I will be proud!"
Chris:	I've even got to write a thank-you letter… that's probably why she keeps sending them… She thinks I like them.
Tammy:	"Tell her what a loverly colour it is… yellow… ooh! Loverly!" Vomit or what!
Chris:	Swap?
Tammy:	No way!
Chris:	Worth a try!
Tammy:	Not really!
Chris:	Come on… let's go to the park?
Tammy:	Whatever!
Chris:	I'm not racing!
Tammy:	Didn't say you had to!
Chris:	You would have

Chicken!

Tammy:	What are you on?
Chris:	My new bike!
Tammy:	Funny!
Tammy & Chris:	Riding to the park we see some mates from school.
Chris:	They can't believe the bikes we're on…
Tammy:	… then Chris shouts out…
Chris:	Yo!
Tammy:	Uncool!
Chris:	Riding to the park, I think I'll do some tricks. A wheelie, an endo and a double flick.
Tammy:	Whack on the brakes and do a skid "Chris has anybody told you you're a real sad kid!"
Chris:	Yeh. But I'm changing! Today is not only Christmas day… today is a turning point in my life. *(He starts to take on superhero persona.)*
Tammy:	A what?
Chris:	The dawning of a new era.
Tammy:	What?
Chris:	I am a mean machine.
Tammy:	More like a micro machine!
Chris:	Shut-up!! I'm where it's at… I am where it's happening… Christopher "super-hero" Simpson!
Tammy:	More like Christopher Robin with your friend Winnie the Pooh! *(reminding him of jumper)*
Chris:	And Gary "I think I'm a hero" Nelson had better watch out.

Section 2

Tammy:	Why's that then Chris?
Chris:	He's only gone and stolen…
Tammy:	Stolen what?
Chris:	Linda Radcliffe.
Tammy:	Yeh, good one!
Chris:	What do you mean?
Tammy:	Gary "I think I'm a hero" Nelson chucked her last week.
Chris:	How do you know?
Tammy:	I sort of made him do it! I said… "if you want to go out with me… you can't still be going out with her." – that's two-timing, isn't it.
Chris:	You're going out with…
Tammy & Chris:	Gary "I think I'm a hero" Nelson!?
Tammy:	Yeh. So you Chris, are free to ask Linda Radcliffe out whenever you want… and all thanks to me.
Chris:	I'll phone her when I get back then.
Tammy:	On Christmas Day?
Chris:	It'd be a sort of… extra Christmas present for her.
Tammy:	Like your jumper from Aunt Ermintrude was for you.
Chris:	What're you trying to say?
Tammy:	Joke!
Chris:	Come on lets go back to my place and phone her.

Section 3:   A Reprimand from Mum

(Chris's house. Chris & Tammy arrive home carrying helmets.)

Ann:	How were the bikes then?
Tammy & Chris:	Fine.
Ann:	And the helmets?
Tammy:	Mine's cool.
Ann:	What about yours Chris?
Chris:	Mine?
Ann:	Yes. Yours.
Chris:	You know what I think about mine.
Ann:	I don't care what you think… as long as you wear it! *(Silence.)* You did wear it didn't you? *(Silence.)* Chris? *(Silence.)* Tammy… he did wear it, didn't he?
Tammy:	*(Starting to exit.)* I'd better be going now… Dad's just got broadband and there's loads of tunes I want to download *(addressing this to Chris)*… on my new mp3 player from Aunt Ermintrude.
Ann:	That was nice of her… she got Chris this lovely jumper, didn't she Chris?
Chris:	Yeh she did Mum.
Ann:	Anyway… where was I? Oh yes I was asking Tammy…
Tammy:	Didn't I give you an answer?
Ann:	No you didn't!
Tammy:	Sorry… what was the question?
Chris:	*(Suddenly shouts out.)* I didn't wear the stupid thing… *(Silence. Freeze.)* *(Quieter)* I look like a wally in it.

Section 3

Ann:	I will not tolerate being spoken to in that way in my house.
Chris:	Shall we go to the garden then?
Ann:	Christopher!
Chris:	I'm not going to wear it… not ever, no matter what you say!
Ann:	What ever has got into you?
Chris:	You're always trying to make me look stupid. Kids at school still call me "Brief-case" because you made me go to school on my first day with some stupid leather brief case…
Ann:	It wasn't stupid… it belonged to your grandfather.
Chris:	Exactly. You told me everyone at Secondary school would have one!
Tammy:	Errrrm, is it alright if I go now, Auntie Ann?
Ann:	I forgot you were there lovey. Bye-bye Tammy.
Tammy:	See you Chris! *(She exits.)*
Ann:	What a fuss! What an embarrassment… and in front of Tammy too.
Chris:	As if she cares!
Ann:	I just want you to wear your cycle helmet. I don't understand why you have to be so awkward about it?
Chris:	No-one else wears them!
Ann:	Tammy was wearing hers, wasn't she?
Chris:	Tammy's a girl!
Ann:	What difference does that make these days.
Chris:	Quite a bit really.

Ann:	Your friend Gary Nelson wears one. I've seen him.
Chris:	Number one… Gary Nelson is not my "friend"
Ann:	He was!
Chris:	Well he's not any more…
Ann:	Oh I can't keep up with you and your friends…
Chris:	*(Interrupting.)* And number two. Gary Nelson is sad!
Ann:	He always looks happy enough to me!
Chris:	*(Sarcastically)* Ha ha ha! Mum, if you're cool… you don't wear them.
Ann:	They all wear them in Neighbours.
Chris:	Neighbours ain't cool… anyway they're in Australia…
Ann:	What's that got to do with it?
Chris:	It's more dangerous! They're all upside down over there.
Ann:	*(Copying Chris)* Ha ha ha! If you want to use your bike, you've got to wear your helmet. And if you won't we'll just lock it in the garage until you change your mind.
Chris:	Go on then!
Ann:	Now you're being "sad"!
Chris:	*(Creeping)* Muuuuum. I'll do you a deal.
Ann:	Try me.
Chris:	I'll wear it… all the time… except for the journeys to and from school.
Ann:	No! It's dangerous.
Chris:	*(Imitating.)* "It's dangerous!"

(Normal voice.) So is walking to school.

Ann: Not if you're sensible. You don't have to cross any main roads… not with the subway. If you want to ride your bike anywhere you will have to wear your helmet. Your school should make it a rule. If everyone had to wear one, no one would take the Micky.

Chris: Well they won't. Our school only makes stupid rules.

Ann: So you agree it is sensible… I know! I'll pop up to school at the beginning of term and have a word with your teacher about it.
(She exits triumphantly.)

Chris: Mum! You're so embarrassing!
Anyway you're not going to change my mind so you can lock it up where you like. It'll stay there and it'll never get used cos there's no way I'm going to wear the stupid thing. No way!

Section 4:   Valentines Disco

Tammy & Chris:	*(Both are wearing cycle helmets.)* Holidays fly by and soon we're back to school.
Tammy & Chris:	Riding our new bikes and feeling real cool.
Tammy:	*(Taking off her helmet.)* Chris always wears his helmet now, I wonder what his mum said.
Chris:	*(Taking off his helmet.)* It's got nothing to do with my mum… I don't want a smashed up head!
Tammy:	When you wouldn't wear it, I thought you were really dumb.
Chris:	Oh, stop going on Tammy – you sound just like my mum! Tammy, she seems to have altered. She doesn't seem quite the same. My mum said she's "growing up too fast… and her boyfriend Gary's to blame! She's got a boyfriend… I haven't even had a snog… And when I asked Linda Radcliffe out she said she'd rather snog a dog. Gary is a pain… he's going out with my best mate. But I won't let him split us… Tam' and I shan't separate.
Tammy:	I get on well with Chris… he's my cousin and he's ok to me But since I've been with Gary, it's him I want to see. I see Chris every morning, but we don't talk much no more I hate to "dis" him, but… he is silly and immature.
Tammy & Chris:	February the fourteenth, our friendship seems to end.
Chris:	Tammy drives me round the bend!

Section 4

Tammy:	It's over something so pathetic… School Valentines Disco. I mean, I promised Gary that I'd go with him, and Chris, the little saddo… says to me "You've got to make a choice! Him or me!"… like we were a couple or something!
	But that don't stop me from feeling guilty… well a bit… but I'll survive… cos Gary's gorgeous… *(Ray, dressed in a suit and carrying a briefcase, enters silently behind Tammy who remains unaware of his presence.)* School disco's are a laugh and I'm up for it cos this is my first with a proper boyfriend. *(She sings a current song as she gets ready.)*
Ray:	Tam?
Tammy:	Dad, how long have you been there?
Ray:	What do you mean?
Tammy:	I didn't know you were there.
Ray:	Why are you having a go at me when I'm about to…
Tammy:	What?
Ray:	Well I know it's too late for tonight… but…
Tammy:	What're you going on about?
Ray:	How about this? *(Hands a card to Tammy who opens it.)*
Tammy:	A card… why?
Ray:	Open it
Tammy:	What? Forty quid? That's a bit random! Why?
Ray:	I want you to go and buy yourself some clothes.
Tammy:	Cool!

Ray:	I wanted to do it at the weekend but the money hadn't cleared… so…
Tammy:	*(Hugging him)* That's amazing! What's the catch?
Ray:	No catch… well… one maybe… I don't want you spending it on piercings or anything.
Tammy:	*(Laughing)* As if! Thanks Dad… that's so cool! I'm gonna get… whoa I can get virtually anything! Can I go tomorrow after school?
Ray:	Course you can. Don't take the money to school though. When's the disco finish?
Tammy:	Nine.
Ray:	And Gary's bringing you back?
Tammy:	Yeh.
Ray:	Be home by half nine then yeh?
Tammy:	Easy. What time does your meeting finish?
Ray:	Nine. So I should be here. And he's picking you up?
Tammy:	We're meeting at the subway.
Ray:	Why can't he pick you up from here? Hasn't there been some bother there?
Tammy:	It's only Nut-Job.
Ray:	Nut-Job?
Tammy:	Ian Sturrock… and his massive. They're just some year elevens at school. They think they're hard.
Ray:	Are they?
Tammy:	*(Laughs)* No!
Ray:	You be careful.
Tammy:	Blatantly.

Section 4

Ray:	Is Chris going?
Tammy:	*(Laughing)* He's not allowed.
Ray:	Oh?
Tammy:	You know what Auntie Ann's like. *(Imitating)* "I don't want my Christopher going to a disco. There'll be too many ruffians there and he'll end up in trouble! He's far too young for that kind of thing!
Ray:	Careful, that's my sister you're laughing at. Do you want a lift?
Tammy:	No, I don't want you embarrassing me.
Ray:	As if I'd do that!
Tammy:	As if!
Ray:	See you later. Don't forget. Half nine!
Tammy:	See ya!
	(Exits in a hurry.)
Nut-Job:	*(Entering loudly.)* Nut-Job.
Massive:	Nut-Job's massive! *(Massive can repeat key words to comic effect and are always Nut-Job's shadow.)*
Nut-Job:	Where's the rest of the Massive?
Massive:	School Disco
Nut-Job:	Nut-Job. I bet you've heard gory tales of Nut-Job
Massive:	And his massive.
Nut-Job:	Nut-Job
Massive:	… and his massive

Nut-Job:	… don't do school Discos. They like to watch people climb up the bank to cross the road to avoid Nut Job
Massive:	… and his massive!
Nut-Job:	Nut Job hangs around looking mean. Sometimes… some dudes tries to walk through Nut-Job's subway…
Massive:	… they don't try it twice…
Nut-Job:	… not if they value their life… not if they value eight pints of blood running through their veins…
Massive:	Nut-Job values his eight pints.
Nut-Job:	What's this? Nut-Job spies some dude coming this way. Nut-Job strike up a mean pose.
Massive:	… and so do his massive!
Nut-Job:	Nut-Job is a bit confused. This ain't no dude.
Massive:	This is a little Year 9 kid!
Nut-Job:	… and he's getting closer.
Massive:	… and closer!
Nut-Job:	Nut-Job stands his ground and hollers: Oi… You!
Massive:	I'n't he so manly!
Gary:	*(Innocently.)* Who me?
Nut-Job:	What's your name… little Year 9.
Gary:	Gary Nelson.
Nut-Job:	Nut-Job wants to know who said you could pass through this subway… Nut Job's Subway?
Gary:	I said I'd meet my girlfriend here.

Section 4

Nut-Job:	You've got a girlfriend?!
Gary:	Yeh… sorry.
Nut-Job:	"Sorry"… is not good enough little Year 9. *(Picking Gary up by the scruff of his neck.)* Nut-Job wants you to beg for mercy and hand over all your money!
Massive:	Hand over all your money!
Tammy:	*(Entering)* No way Gary!
Nut-Job:	Eh?
Tammy:	No way Nut-Job. Put him down!
Nut-Job:	Tammy Eccles… the fittest bird on this manor. Nut-Job can't believe you're going out with him. Why don't you come over here and give Nut-Job a big sloppy kiss. *(Tammy ducks out of the way, leaving Nut-Job and Massive to kiss, realise what they have done, make lots of "yeuch!" noises, and during the confusion, Tammy and Gary get through the subway.)*
Nut-Job & Massive:	*(After composing themselves, looking at where Tammy and Gary were.)* Where've you gone?
Tammy & Gary:	Through the subway!
Tammy:	Nut-Job, can't you find anything better to do than terrorise kids in Year 9… after all, it is… Valentine's night?
Nut-Job:	Nut-Job's girl-friend dumped him.
Massive:	Dumped him – ha ha ha! *(Nut-Job pulls The Massive's hat over his eyes, or some other humiliating gesture!)*
Tammy:	Good for her! Get a life Nut-Job.
Nut-Job:	If you were a bloke, Nut-Job would slap you!

Tammy:	Well, I'm not… so sling your hook Nut-Job! *(Nut-Job exits, simpering.)*
Massive:	Yeh, sling your hook!
Nut-Job:	Why don't you just get lost!
Massive:	No, you get lost!
Nut-Job:	No, you get lost!
Massive:	No, you get lost!
Nut-Job:	No, you get lost!
Massive:	Do you know what. We don't even like you anymore. *(Exit.)*
Nut-Job:	I didn't mean it! Come back! Please! *(Exit.)*
Gary:	Well, now we've sorted him for you, I can give you this.
Tammy:	Gary? A red rose! How romantic. Did you get my card?
Gary:	Yeh.
Tammy:	I meant what I said in it.
Gary:	Did you? I'm gonna enjoy tonight then!
Tammy:	So… to the disco?
Gary:	Blatantly!
Tammy:	You'll dance with me.
Gary:	Course.
Tammy:	Even though your mates'll be there.
Gary:	Tammy… I want them to see!
	(Sudden loud music and Tammy and Gary dance together making the most of any opportunity to be

Section 4

humourous. The audience can become involved in the dance routine too. After a while the music fades slightly for the following dialogue.)

Gary: Oh yeah, what did you say to Chris after school?

Tammy: Why?

Gary: He was well upset.

Tammy: I just got stressed with him. He can be such an idiot sometimes.

Gary: Maybe it'll do him some good… you know…

Tammy: No… I was well over the top.

Gary: What did you say to him?

Tammy: I was really cruel… I'll phone him tomorrow… in the morning. We'll cycle to school together… get it sorted.

Gary: I'm sure he'll forgive you. I would. *(Music changes to slow romantic song.)*

Gary & Tammy: And then they played a slow one
                     We'd been waiting all night for this
                     Time to dance close together
                     And have our very first kiss.

                     (Romantic music swells as they consult with the audience what they should do. As they approach each other, they nervously clinch and then kiss. When the music fades, their clinch and slow dancing continues until…)

Tammy: *(Looking at watch.)* Gary… look at the time… ten o'clock… my dad'll go mental!

Gary: He's sorted, your dad.

Tammy: He is usually… but…

Gary & Tammy: Come on… let's run!

Tammy:	I said goodnight to Gary at the corner of the street. The front room light's on… dad's still up… I walk in… all discrete. *(Enters.)* What?! Dad's not in… what a relief… I thought I'd get loads of grief. I know what I'll surf the net… there's loads of tunes I want to get. At least he didn't have to wait… he'll have no idea that I was late.
Ray:	I've been out looking for you!
Tammy:	What?
Ray:	*(Looking at his watch.)* Ten past ten… you said you'd be back by half nine. I rang your mobile but you didn't answer.
Tammy:	I didn't hear it!
Ray:	It doesn't take you an hour to get home from school.
Tammy:	*(With a wry grin.)* It did tonight!
Ray:	I want to know where you've been, what you've been up to?
Tammy:	I haven't been "up to" anything!
Ray:	I'm not stupid! You've "blatantly" been doing something.
Tammy:	Gary walked me home… I don't know… we were chatting.
Ray:	Chatting! Tammy. For over an hour! I've been really worried. I've even phoned the school!
Tammy:	No-one would be there you idiot!
Ray:	Don't you speak to me like that!

Section 4

Tammy:	Whatever!
Ray:	If you'd been much longer I'd've phoned the police
Tammy:	You often get home later than you say and I don't go phoning your office or telling the police.
Ray:	That's different.
Tammy:	It's not!
Ray:	If I stay on at work, it's to get enough money to make our lives more comfortable… and you know that!
Tammy:	But you're never here!
Ray:	That's not the point… and it's not true! If you want to be treated like an adult you've…
Ray & Tammy:	*(interrupting)*… got to behave like one.
Ray:	I wouldn't push it if I were you.
Tammy:	I'm off to bed.
Ray:	Right! If that's all you've got to say, I'll ground you for the rest of the week…
Tammy:	No way!
Ray:	And I'm not discussing it!
Tammy:	But you said I could go to town tomorrow after school… and…
Ray:	No!
Tammy:	Gary and me are going to the fair on Friday.
Ray:	<u>Were</u> going to the fair.
Tammy:	Dad!
Ray:	I can't imagine his parents'll be too happy about tonight either.

Tammy: They won't mind… they probably won't even be in!

Ray: I'm not having this Tammy.

Tammy: You're just jealous!

Ray: What do you mean?

Tammy: Oh… tut… it doesn't matter.

Ray: It does.

Tammy: I'm going to bed.

Ray: Tammy! You said I was jealous. What did you mean?

Tammy: *(Pause.)* You're jealous 'cos you haven't got anybody. Sorry dad, but it's true.
(Exits.)

Section 5:　　The Accident

Chris:	Right since we were little kids, Tammy was my best mate Did everything together... life was simple... we were great Yesterday things changed... moved on... I don't really understand So today I'm going to school on my own... I don't need her to hold my hand. I wash, get dressed just like normal listening to Radio One. Then consider bunking school... yeah... cool... maybe not... knowing my luck I'd get done! So I lift the garage door vowing "To Tammy I will not talk!" *(Sees his bike.)* Oh what! I've got a puncture... I'm gonna have to walk!
Ann:	Christopher... are you still here darling?
Chris:	Yes, I am... and don't call me darling... or Christopher for that matter!
Ann:	There's no need to bite my head off! Tammy's on the phone for you.
Chris:	Tammy? What do you want?
Tammy:	Chris, I'm sorry about yesterday. Do you want to cycle to school with me?
Chris:	I can't.
Tammy:	*(Resigned.)* Oh, alright. I just thought... you know...
Chris:	Not "I don't want to"... I can't... I've got a puncture.
Tammy:	Let's walk then?
Chris:	Seriously?
Tammy:	*(Sarcastically.)* I've never been so serious in all my life!

Chris:	*(Looking at his watch.)* We'll have to run…
Tammy:	See you at the swings!
Tammy & Chris:	*(Suddenly together.)* Sorted!
	(Creating a different scene in a different area of the stage.)
Liz:	*(Calling out)* Gary… Gary!
Gary:	*(Off)* What?
Liz:	It's half past eight.
Gary:	*(Off)* Where's mum? Oh Liz, why didn't you wake me up?
Liz:	What do you think I am doing now?
Gary:	*(Entering)* I'll never get to school on time and we've got a test!
Liz:	A test, the night after a school disco? That's stupid!
Gary:	Liz, can you give us a lift… please… you are the coolest sister anyone could ever have!
Liz:	*(Pretending to think about it.)* Ummmmmmm. *(Owning up)* I was going to give you one anyway… mum said you'd be tired so I should let you sleep in a bit. You want to get there in time for the test then?
Gary:	Course I do! It'll be easy!
Liz:	Oh, will it now?!!
	(Back to the Chris & Tammy Scene.)
Chris:	*(Lively.)* Alright?
Tammy:	Alright! Did you mind me phoning?
Chris:	No… 's cool. How was it last night?

Section 5

Tammy:	Awesome… you should have gone!
Chris:	I would have done… if I was allowed.
Tammy:	My dad went mental with me after.
Chris:	Why?
Tammy:	I got back late.
Chris:	What time?
Tammy:	Nearly half ten.
Chris:	What were you up to?
Tammy:	*(Conspiring)* Do you really want to know?
Chris:	Yeh.
Tammy:	Can you keep a secret?
Chris:	Yeh!
Tammy:	Well, after the disco, me and Gary were walking down the street, and he says "let's nick that car".
Chris:	Wow!
Tammy:	So he breaks in…
Chris:	Yeh?
Tammy:	… hot-wires it…
Chris:	No?
Tammy:	… and we're off down the road.
Chris:	That's not like Gary!
Tammy:	Then he says "let's ram raid the jewellers"
Chris:	*(Shocked)* Tammy!
Tammy:	*(Speaking fast so Chris can't interrupt.)* So we crash into the front of it, Gary gets out, scoops up

all the jewels and he gives me a hundred diamond rings!

Chris: *(Having been with the story all the way.)* Really?

Tammy: No you idiot! He just walked me home and we lost track of the time.

Chris: But the disco was good.

Tammy: Blatantly!

Chris: Come on… we'd better get to school.

(Cross to Gary & Liz… now in a car… Liz obviously in the driving seat. Gary yawns.)

Liz: Good night last night?

Gary: Ok.

Liz: What does that mean?

Gary: I've been seeing her for two months… well… eight weeks! It's a long time.

Liz: You sound like you want a change?

Gary: Probably. Do you think you'll marry Martin?

Liz: He'll have to divorce football before I even consider it.

Gary: Do you think I look like George Clooney?

Liz: Why do you ask?

Gary: Tammy thinks I do.

Liz: She probably meant Wayne Rooney!

Gary: I don't think so!

(Back to the Chris & Tammy scene.)

Tammy: *(Pulling Chris)* Come on, let's go and get some sweets.

Section 5

Chris:	Tammy!
Tammy:	Come on!
Chris:	We're late as it is.
Tammy:	It's only registration… we can get a late!
Chris:	Ok. Guess what? I'm making my debut for the school football team.
Tammy:	I know Gary told me.
Chris:	What did he say?
Tammy:	Just that you were playing.
Chris:	They won't have seen anything like it!
Tammy:	Yeh come to think of it… he said that too!.
Chris:	Cool! Come on then… but please hurry up!
Tammy:	Remember I could have cycled to school!
Tammy & Chris:	Into the shop… grab some sweets Pay at the checkout… and out onto the busy – *(They "mime" cars passing very fast)* – very busy street. *(Cross to Liz's car.)*
Gary:	Oh, I've left my watch at home… what's the time?
Liz:	Quarter to.
Gary:	Come on Liz… hurry up… they won't let me do the test today if I'm not there at the start.
Liz:	Course they will.
Gary:	They won't. They've really tightened up since your time.
Liz:	You're such a swot!

Gary:	Just want to do well that's all.
Liz:	You mean you don't want to mess up like I did.
Gary:	Hey look! *(Hurriedly winding the window down and shouting out of it)* Ange! How's Frankie?
Liz:	Stop it Gary!
Gary:	*(Winding the widow up.)* She's in my class! *(Laughing)* She kissed Frankie Worthington last night… couldn't believe it… she's really nice… he's a total dork!

(Back to the Chris & Tammy Scene)

Chris:	It's raining! Let's run!
Tammy:	I'll race you.
Chris:	No problem. *(They start running)*

(Cross to Liz's car.)

Gary:	If it keeps raining like this our football match'll be postponed.
Liz:	Who are you playing?
Gary:	St. Edmunds.
Liz:	You normally hammer them.
Gary:	We don't normally have "Brief-Case" in goal for us.
Liz:	Who?
Gary:	Briefcase… actually he's Tammy's cousin… he's a right plank!

(Back to the Chris & Tammy Scene)

Chris:	Come on Tammy, cross here or we'll get drenched!
Tammy:	No!
Chris:	Come on. Don't be such a chicken!

Section 5

(Cross to Liz's car)

Liz: Look at this rain!

Gary: Dad said I can have a quid for every goal I score this season… he already owes me eight quid.

Liz: Well you can give it to me for petrol.

Gary: No way! Dad always buys your petrol anyway!

Liz: Only while I'm on the dole.

Gary: That's what I said… always!

Liz: Cheeky monkey!

(Back to the Chris & Tammy Scene)

Chris: Time for Super-Hero Chris Simpson to strut out into the road, to dodge cars that dare to cross his path and slide past speeding motorcycles. He arrives at the other side of the road totally unscathed… adrenaline flowing… heart pounding… and ego… sky high! Yesss!

                 Come on Tammy. You try!

Tammy: No. I'll use the subway.

Chris: "I'll use the subway"… don't be such a chicken.

Tammy: It's not a matter of being a chicken…

Chris: What is it then?

(Cross to Liz's car)

Gary: I'm getting a dvd for my bedroom.

Liz: With what?

Gary: Saving… birthday money… and goal money from Dad!.

Liz: *(Laughing)* You won't score that many!

(Back to the Chris & Tammy scene)

Chris:	You're chicken. *(Taking out his mobile and starting to film Tammy)* Listen everyone! Tammy Eccles is a chicken! I'll show everyone what a chicken you are when we get to school!
Tammy:	It won't come out… I'm too far away.
Chris:	Want a bet?
Tammy:	Chris!
Chris:	Do it… it'll be well impressive!
Tammy:	Alright then?
Chris:	Seriously?
Tammy:	Yeh. I'll make it worth while!
Chris:	Come on then…
Tammy:	Pause it for a minute. The cars were miles away when you crossed. See that red car… I'll start when it reaches this lamppost. Ready?
Chris:	Come on then quick!
Tammy:	Ready to record?
Chris:	*(Sudden realisation)* Tammy! You sure!
Voices:	*(A chant of "Chicken" is repeated rhythmically by the actors playing Liz and Gary to create an atmosphere of impending disaster/tragedy.)*
Tammy:	Course! Just make sure you get this on your phone you wus!
Chris:	Go on then… quick.
Tammy:	After the lamp-post!
Chris:	Now!

Section 5

Tammy:	No! *(Tammy hesitates, then finally steps into the road in front of Liz's car.)* Now!
Chris:	Tammy!
All:	No!!!
	(Tammy is hit and falls. This staging of the accident should contain the main elements of this accident… i.e. impending danger, speed, screams/ noise and impact.
	Sudden silence.
	Realisation sets in. Possible use of slow motion?)
Chris:	*(To audience)* I didn't think she'd do it.
Liz:	*(Disbelievingly approaching Chris)* What was she playing at?
Chris:	I don't know!
Liz:	*(Moving towards Chris… in shock… hesitant but gaining in confidence.)* She just ran our in front of me… You must have seen something…
Chris:	I didn't!
Liz:	Why would she do that?
Chris:	I don't know! I don't know anything!
Gary:	Liz! Liz! It's Tammy! *(Silence)*
Chris:	While nobody was looking I slid the phone down a drain I knew if anybody found it… I'd get the blame… People'd say I'd encouraged her with a dare They'd make judgements and suspect I didn't care They'd say I should've known better… should have been more mature

But everyone knows... for a moment's stupidity
there is no known cure
Believe me... I'd do anything to change what
happened that day.
The day I saw Tammy's body on the dual
carriageway...
Being totally covered by a blanket, then stretchered
away...

*(Tammy and any other debris are cleared away. It
is entirely acceptable for Tammy to walk off stage
with minimal fuss.)*

The funeral was awful, the church was packed
Everybody went.
I'll never forget her coffin, covered in the flowers
that everyone'd sent.
Tammy's Dad sat next to my mum... together in
their grief
She held his hand as the vicar talked of Tammy's
life, saying it was "all too brief".
And then... then they played her favourite song
and everyone cried.
Everyone apart from me... I felt numb...
something inside me had died.

Gary: *(Approaches Chris in silence.)*
Chris... we should talk.

Chris: Should we?

Gary: I thought you might want to.

Chris: Well, you're wrong.

Gary: Why don't you want to talk to me?

(Silence.)

Do you blame my sister? Chris is that why you
won't talk to me? Liz wouldn't have been driving
along that road if it wasn't for me... so... so...
was it my fault?

Section 5

Chris: I'm not saying it was anyone's fault!

Gary: But others are… aren't they? That's the whole
                point. I didn't see anything… and nor did Liz… and
                people are blaming her. But you were with Tammy,
                so if anyone knows why she ran out like that, its
                you.
                (Silence.)

                (Exasperated) Why won't you tell me?

Ann: *(Entering.)* Chris I've got you something.
                *(He looks up. She hands him a little giftwrapped
                present. He opens it revealing a mobile phone in
                a box.)*

                I know I said I wouldn't get you another one but…
                well, it's been difficult for you… and well… aren't
                you going to say anything?

Chris: Who am I going to phone now Tammy's gone…

Ann: Chris? How can you say such a thing?

Chris: Easily.

Ann: I thought you'd like it! I thought you'd be grateful. I
                should have known better! Chris I'm talking to you.
                (Silence.)
                You can't go on like this! It's been nearly a month
                since the accident and you've hardly been out of
                the house. Your Head of Year phoned and he says
                you should be back in school on Monday.

Chris: I can't! Everybody'll treating me different… and
                Gary said… well he's blaming me… he's probably
                made everyone think I know something when I
                don't. I can't face all the questions mum… I
                thought it'd end once the police had talked to
                me… but… there's kids at school and then there's
                the inquest that's not going to be for ages either…
                and now you're starting! And there's something
                else. I can't cope with seeing Tammy's Dad.

Chicken!

Ann:	He's certainly not blaming you.
Chris:	I know… but…
Ann:	But what?
Chris:	He's been really good… really kind… but… couldn't we move?
Ann:	What?
Chris:	Couldn't we move house… start again away from everyone.
Ann:	Then it really would look like you're running away from something.
Chris:	I just wish it hadn't happened.
Ann:	I just wish someone had been there… you know… a witness… to see what happened… to see why she… I'm sorry Chris. I don't really know what to do either… but I do think you need to get back to some kind of normality…
Chris:	Life'll never be normal after this.
Ann:	You know Chris… sometimes I get the impression you are blaming yourself… it's not your fault… you were on the other side of the road, weren't you? How could it be anything to do with you?
Chris:	To this day I've not told anyone the words <u>you</u> know I said Someone, somehow finding out is the one thing I most dread. I think about it every day, every night before I fall asleep. A secret I must live with; a secret I must keep.
	(He stares at the phone, which remains unpacked. He slowly exits as music builds.)

Other plays published by **dbda**

If you have enjoyed reading and/or working with this playscript, you may like to find out about other plays we publish. There are brief descriptions and other details on the following pages.

All plays deal with contemporary social and moral issues and are suitable for Youth Theatres, Schools, Colleges, and adult AmDram. They are ideal for GCSE Drama/English exam use and frequently do well in One Act Play Festivals. They offer both male and female performers equally challenging opportunities.

For enquiries or to order plays published by dbda, please contact:
dbda, Pin Point, Rosslyn Crescent, Harrow HA1 2SB.
Tel: 0870 333 7771
Fax: 0870 333 7772
Email: info@dbda.co.uk

All enquiries regarding performing rights of plays by
Mark Wheeller, should be made to:
Sophie Gorel Barnes, MBA Literary Agents,
62 Grafton Way, London W1P 5LD.
Tel: 020 7387 2076
Email: sophie@mbalit.co.uk

All enquiries regarding performing rights of 'Heroin Lies'
by Wayne Denfhy, should be made to:
Wayne Denfhy, c/o **dbda**,
Pin Point, Rosslyn Crescent, Harrow HA1 2SB.
Tel: 0870 333 7771
Email: info@dbda.co.uk (subject: Wayne Denfhy)

All enquiries regarding performing rights of 'Gagging For It'
by Danny Sturrock, should be made to:
Danny Sturrock, c/o **dbda**,
Pin Point, Rosslyn Crescent, Harrow HA1 2SB.
Tel: 0870 333 7771
Email: info@dbda.co.uk (subject: Danny Sturrock)

Forthcoming plays (to be published in 2007)

KILL JILL by Mark Wheeller
Commissioned and premiered by the Birmingham Rep Theatre

This One Act Play uses ideas form the age-old story of *Jack & the Beanstalk* with a bit of *Kill Bill* thrown in for good measure! Jack has been repeatedly robbing the guy at the top of the beanstalk, but his final visit is different. His girlfriend, Jill (of course!), accompanies him on the day when the victim of these robberies has chosen this day to lay in wait for the young thieves, armed with a shotgun. The ending is suitably Tarantinoesque. *Kill Jill* raises issues of rights and responsibilities. It is a play full of interesting techniques that will delight Drama teachers and students and will thrill those exploring Citizenship issues through imaginative and entertaining Theatre productions.

"What a great script! Powerful stuff! At times the dialogue's quite surreal – I love the Panto moments – e.g. having the cow mooing inconspicuously until the final blurting out in Ali G speak! Wonderful stuff!!!!! I found the build up of tension in the visit to George's castle and the scene between Jill and George started to put the play in firm thriller territory! … Kill Jill is a very fizzy ride!"

Paul Mills, Head of Drama, Westgate School, Winchester

BANG OUT OF ORDER by Johnny Carrington & Danny Sturrock

Supported by Southampton City Council, the play was awarded a Home Office 'Taking A Stand' award in April 2006.

6 friends, 1 secret, 1 chance, 1 life. An anti-social rollercoaster ride with comedy, music and opportunities for multi-media. A new energetic piece which will educate, amuse and challenge. Set on an urban estate, newcomer Ollie has a history of antisocial behaviour and is attempting to reform, but once he is accepted into the local group of youths, things start to go wrong.

"If you are setting out to convey a message, the mixture of naturalism which pulls no punches, stylised movement that moves the action along with wit and mixed media that adds another dimension, certainly grabbed the attention of the audience."

Fran Morley, Youth & Community Director, Nuffield Theatre Southampton

"A production that was both entertaining and thought-provoking."

Jeannie Russell, Adjudicator Totton Drama Festival

The Story of Wacky Soap is a modern day cautionary tale

Wacky Soap looks just like any soap but the Everyday Folk of the Bower of Bliss soon realise that it has special powers; washing with it makes people do wacky things… they begin to behave like elephants, trumpeting loudly and squirting water everywhere. Those who wash with Wacky Soap for longer find that it also has other, dangerous powers…

How do the Everyday Folk of the Bower of Bliss deal with this Wacky invention?

What happened to the beautiful Princess Symbol who mysteriously disappeared overnight?

What does King Huff, the inventor of Wacky Soap, has to say about all the wacky things happening in his kingdom?

Read the story to find out…

I've done it! bubbled King Huff so excited that, for once, he forgot to speak in rhyme.

The smelly Queen Huff was so busy mending the brakes on her Royal motorbike, that she didn't hear him.

Their daughter, the teenage Princess Symbol, was in her headphones, because everyone in Bliss Palace had been complaining about her music… so she didn't hear him.

The Palace guards, courtiers and servants were carrying out their everyday duties, so they didn't hear him either.

In fact, no one in Bliss Palace knew what it was, that King Huff had done. No one except for the Kings trusty rubber duck. He knew that King Huff had done something quite amazing and quacked very loudly.

5

Somebody threw a half used bar of Wacky Soap at King Huff, nearly knocking his crown to the ground. Trusty was shocked and quacked noisily.

Wacky Soap must be banned! chanted the crowd. Many of the Everyday Folk were upset, tears streaming down their faces. Suddenly Queen Huff appeared on the Royal balcony. She was in quite a state, too!

King Huff, King Huff, I have something to tell! Not now, my dear, I have a riot to quell!

But the sweetly scented Queen was not to be silenced. Last night Princess Symbol washed in her Royal shower. She used your Wacky Soap hour after hour. This morning when I went to see er I found that she had completely disappear..d Poor girl… she must have washed herself clean away For there on her bed… were two empty crates of Wacky Soap and her favourite negligee!

Trusty looked at King Huff and saw that, for the second time in this story, he was lost for a rhyme.

25

24

The story of Wacky Soap first appeared as a **Musical play**. A mini version of the musical, adapted for Junior Schools, is included with the **Music Score**.

The **Storybook**, as well as being a wonderful book to read on its own, is often used for inspiration with props and costumes for the play.

A **Past-performance CD** gives you the opportunity to hear the songs of the play, while a fully orchestrated **Backing track CD** will be invaluable to those who want to produce the play but do not have music facilities.

Past performance CD
Price: £15.00 each

ISBN 1 902843 07 X

A fully illustrated book with the story of Wacky Soap in narrative form.

Price: £ 6.95 per book / £90.00 for a set of 15

ISBN 1 902843 06 1

*A companion book containing a **Mini-Musical** version for Junior Schools.*
Duration: 40 mins

Price: £ 4.95 per book / £65.00 for a set of 15

Backing track CD
Price: £25.00 each

"Wacky Soap' was an outstanding success!!!...
We have had letters from people in the audience
saying what a fab show it was and how impressed
they were. The most frequent comment was that
it was a 'risk' to put it on as a school show
(as opposed to doing 'Oliver' or 'Little Shop of
Horrors') and one that thoroughly paid off!!
'The feel good factor was amazing' was another
comment we had. Many people said how
impressed they were by the 'community' spirit of
the production - everybody working together
without the 'star' element creeping in!"

John Plant, Head of Drama
Southmoor School, Sunderland

Other plays published by **dbda**

ISBN 1 902843 17 1

Cast: 3f, 3m &3m/f or 3m & 3f for GCSE using suggested cuts
Duration: 55 minutes approx.
KS 3 & 4

Gagging for it by Danny Sturrock

Summer is here, A-levels are over and a group of 6 friends embark on a holiday to Ibiza! What would their holiday bring? Would Chris finally pluck up the courage to ask out Teresa? Would Jay drink himself into oblivion? Would Bianca spend the entire holiday flirting with the Spanish barmen – more than likely! ...or would their experiments with drugs bring their hedonistic worlds crashing down around them!?

Comedy, dance music and choreography are the keys to this production. The pace is breakneck and hilarious, but once the party's over, it hits you!

'Really funny... laugh out loud funny. Inspired outstanding performances from the six Year 11s who went on to exceed our expectations by a long way in their GCSEs achieving A or A*. It proved to be a firm favourite with our KS3/4 audience.'

Mark Wheeller

ISBN 1 902843 15 0

Cast: 8f, 7m and 2m/f
Duration: 70 minutes approx.
KS 3 & 4

Heroin Lies by Wayne Denfhy

A sensitive, yet disturbing look at drugs and drug dependency, in particular the pressures and influences at play on an ordinary teenage girl. We observe Vicki's gradual and tragic slide towards addiction and also the various degrees of help and hindrance she receives from family and friends.

This is a new, updated edition of Wayne Denfhy's popular play. It is suitable for performance as well as for reading in the class. Included with the playscript is an excellent scheme for follow-up work by Peter Rowlands.

'...a piece of drama that will stimulate and challenge a young cast... Heroin Lies deals with vital issues that affect today's youngsters in a gentle and humane way and, in so doing, gets its message across without the instant rejection that can meet other approaches.'

Pete Sanpher, Head of Drama, Norfolk

The Gate Escape by Mark Wheeller

The story of two truants. Corey is 'addicted' to bunking school. Chalkie views himself as a casual truant "no problem!" While truanting with some friends, the pair are greeted by a surreal 'Big Brother' figure who sets them a task. The loser will be in for some dramatic 'Big Bother'... Who will lose?... What will this 'bother' be?

The play has toured professionally throughout the south of England to great acclaim.

'A lively dramatic style and innovative structure with dynamic and contemporary dialogue. It is written in a way to guarantee that the audience will feel fully involved and enthralled by the main characters.'

ISBN 1 902843 14 2

Professor Ken Reid, Author of Tackling Truancy in Schools

Cast: *2f & 2m with doubling, or up to 30*
Duration: *70 minutes approx.*
KS 3 & 4

'Theatrically interesting... excellent basis for active discussion of issues and dramatic style with reluctant GCSE students'

Ali Warren (National Drama)

Too Much Punch for Judy by Mark Wheeller

A hard-hitting documentary play, based on a tragic drink-drive accident that results in the death of Jo, front seat passenger. The driver, her sister Judy, escapes unhurt (or has she?).

The tragic incident was dramatised by Mark in 1986 using only the words of those most closely involved and affected. This play has become one of the most frequently performed plays ever!

'The play will have an impact on young people or adults. It will provoke discussion. It stimulates and wants you to cry out for immediate social action and resolution.'

Henry Shankula – Addiction Research Foundation, Toronto

ISBN 1 902843 05 3

Cast: *2f & 2m with doubling or 3f, 3m & 6*
Duration: *50 minutes approx.*
KS 4 to adult

'The young audience I was sat in was patently out for some whooping Friday night fun... at the end there was a horrid silence.'

Nick Baker – Times Educational Supplement

Other plays published by **dbda**

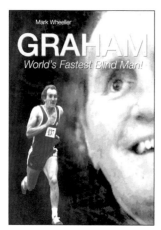

ISBN 1 902843 09 6

Cast: 5m & 4f with doubling, or up to 34
Duration: 80 minutes approx.
KS 3/4 to adult

GRAHAM – World's Fastest Blind Man!
by Mark Wheeller

A play full of lively humour telling the inspirational story of Graham Salmon MBE. Totally blind since birth, Graham went on to become the World's Fastest Blind Man running 100 metres in 11.4 seconds! The play, written in Mark's unique documentary style, skillfully brings to life Graham's courage, tenacity and wonderful sense of humour.

'I'm very proud of my group's response to this play; initially they were interested and admired Graham and Marie but that evolved into a desire to not just tell Graham's story but to celebrate his life! At the end of the performance the cast spontaneously gestured to a picture of Graham and Marie and the audience reacted with warm applause.'

Mike Fleetwood, Parkside Arts College

ISBN 1 902843 16 9

Cast: 2m & 2f with doubling, or up to 18
Duration: 45-50 minutes
KS 3/4 to adult

Missing Dan Nolan (based on a true story)
by Mark Wheeller

This play, based on the true story of Dan Nolan, a teenage boy who went missing on the night of January 1st 2002, is written in the same documentary style as *Too Much Punch for Judy*. It has won awards and commendations at every Drama Festival it has entered. It is now, like so many of Mark's other plays, being toured professionally by the Queens Theatre in Hornchurch, Essex.

'Unusual and deeply affecting. Skillfully written... achieves astonishing depth and authenticity... '

Charles Evans, Adjudicator, Eastleigh Drama Festival

'I feel very proud. All the issues about our Dan's disappearance, and the safety issues surrounding teenagers, are in the play and it will continue to raise awareness'

Pauline Nolan (Dan's mother)

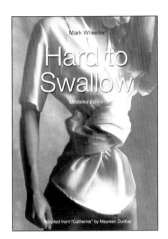

ISBN 1 902843 08 8

Cast: *3f & 2m with doubling, or 6f, 3m & 16*
Duration: *70 minutes*
KS 3 to adult

Hard to Swallow by Mark Wheeller

This play is an adaptation of Maureen Dunbar's award winning book (and film) *Catherine* which charts her daughter's uneven battle with anorexia and the family's difficulties in coping with the illness.

The play has gone on to be performed all over the world to much acclaim, achieving considerable success in One Act Play Festivals. Its simple narrative style means that it is equally suitable for adult and older youth groups to perform.

'This play reaches moments of almost unbearable intensity... naturalistic scenes flow seamlessly into sequences of highly stylised theatre... such potent theatre!'
Vera Lustiq, The Independent

'Uncompromising and sensitive... should be compulsory viewing to anyone connected with the education of teenagers.'
Mick Martin, Times Educational Supplement

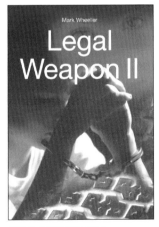

ISBN 1 902843 18 5

Cast: *2f & 2m with doubling*
Duration: *60 minutes approx.*
KS 3 & 4 and A Level

Legal Weapon II by Mark Wheeller

This is a new "improved" version of the popular *Legal Weapon* play which is touring schools across the UK.

It is the story of a young man, Andy. His relationship with his girlfriend – and his car – are both flawed, but his speeding causes the loss of a life and the loss of his freedom.

In *Legal Weapon II*, the story takes an additional twist when Andy realises that the person he's killed is somebody very dear to Jazz, his girlfriend.

Legal Weapon II promises to be faster, funnier and far more powerful!

'A gripping storyline. Even the most challenging of our students were held by the drama. This learning experience should be given to each Year 11 as they come through the school.'
Myrtle Springs Secondary School

Other Plays by Mark Wheeller (not published by dbda)

Sequinned Suits And Platform Boots

Duration: 55 mins   **Cast:** 6f, 7m & 1m or f

Published by: Maverick Musicals: http://www.mavmuse.com/default.asp

A play that seems more like a Musical! Sequinned Suits and Platform Boots is Mark Wheeller's new One Act comedy tribute to the colourful Glam Rock years. It charts (semi-autobiographically) the teenage years of Shakey Threwer and his desperate attempt to be noticed by the Music industry. "Funky & funny... but be warned, it will have you coming away cringing at your own memories of singing into a hairbrush whilst staring at your reflection in the mirror." *Craig Morrison Southampton Institute Newspaper 2005*

Arson About   Script: Mark Wheeller (Ed. Andy Kempe)

Duration: 75 mins   **Cast:** 4 (2f & 2m with doubling)

Published by: Nelson Thornes Ltd. Tel: 01242 267100

Mollie and Ian are hot for each other. Stueey can be a real bright spark. Mr Butcher's comments have inflamed Shuttle. All in all it's combustible material but when you play with fire it can be more than your fingers that get burnt. Arson About is a theatrical power keg which crackles with wit and moves along with a scorching pace. But in this play by Mark Wheeller the cost of 'arson about' becomes all too clear.

Chunnel of Love   Script: Graham Cole & Mark Wheeller

Duration: 100 mins   **Cast:** 25 (11f, 8m & 6m/f)

Published by: Zig Zag Education. Tel: 0117 950 3199

A bi-lingual play (80% English & 20% French) about teenage pregnancy. Lucy is fourteen - she hopes to become a vet and is working hard to gain good grades in her GCSE exams, when she discovers she is pregnant. She faces a series of major decisions, not least of which is what to tell the father... Ideal as a school production and Key Stage 4 Drama course book.

Sweet FA !   Script: Mark Wheeller

Duration: 45 mins plus interval   **Cast:** 3f / 2m (or more)

Published by: SchoolPlay Productions Ltd. Tel: 01206 540111

A Zigger Zagger for girls (and boys)! A new play (also available as a full length Musical) telling the true life story of Southampton girl footballer Sarah Stanbury (Sedge) whose ambition is to play Football (Soccer) for England. Her dad is delighted... her mum disapproves strongly! An ideal GCSE production and Key Stage 4 Drama course book. Drama GCSE scheme of work also available.

Blackout – One Evacuee in Thousands   MUSICAL

Script: Mark Wheeller with the Stantonbury Youth Theatre   **Music:** Mark Wheeller

Duration: 90 mins plus interval   **Published by:** SchoolPlay Productions Ltd.

A Musical about the plight of Rachael Eagle, a fictional evacuee in World War II. Rachel's parents are determined that the war will not split the family up. After refusing to have her evacuated in 1939 they decide to do so midway though 1940. At first Rachael does not settle but, after the death of her mother, she becomes increasingly at home with her billets in Northamptonshire. When her father requests that she return she wants to stay where she feels at home. An ideal large scale school production with good parts for girls (and boys).

For more details and an up-to-date list of plays, please visit Mark's website:
www.amdram.co.uk/wheellerplays *(please note wheeller has two "l")*